Lewis Carroll's

Alice in Wonderland

Lewis Carroll's

Alice in Wonderland

® www.raintreepublishers.co.uk
Visit our website to find out
more information about
Raintree books.

Phone 0845 6044371
Fax +44 (0) 1865 312263
Email myorders@capstonepub.co.uk

Customers from outside the UK please telephone +44 1865 312262

Raintree is an imprint of Capstone Global Library Limited, a company incorporated in
England and Wales having its registered office at 7 Pilgrim Street, London, EC4V 6LB –
Registered company number: 6695582

"Raintree" is a registered trademark of Pearson Education Limited, under licence to
Capstone Global Library Limited

Text © Stone Arch Books 2010
First published in hardback and paperback in the United Kingdom by
Capstone Global Library 2010
The moral rights of the proprietor have been asserted.

Art Director: Bob Lentz
Designer: Brann Garvey
Creative Director: Heather Kindseth
Editorial Director: Michael Dahl
Editor: Donald Lemke
Associate Editor: Sean Tulien
UK Editor: Laura Knowles
Originated by Capstone Global Library Ltd
Printed and bound in China by Leo Paper Products Ltd

ISBN 978 1 406214 14 7 (hardback)
14 13 12 11 10
10 9 8 7 6 5 4 3 2 1

ISBN 978 1 406214 18 5 (paperback)
14 13 12 11 10
10 9 8 7 6 5 4 3 2 1

British Library Cataloguing in Publication Data
A full catalogue record for this book is available from the British Library.

Contents

CAST OF CHARACTERS.................................. 4

CHAPTER 1
Down the Rabbit Hole............................ 6

CHAPTER 2
The Pool of Tears................................ 12

CHAPTER 3
Advice from a Caterpillar 25

CHAPTER 4
A Mad Tea Party................................ 36

CHAPTER 5
The Terrible Queen 42

CHAPTER 6
The Mock Turtle's Story 50

CHAPTER 7
Alice's Evidence................................ 55

Carroll's Characters............................. 64
About the Author and Illustrator 66
Glossary 67
Discussion Questions........................... 68
Writing Prompts 69

Cast of Characters

Cheshire Cat

White Rabbit

Alice

King and Queen of Hearts

Caterpillar

Mad Hatter

5

17

"Fury said to a mouse, that he met in the house, 'Let us both go to law: I w come, I'll take no denial: We must have the trial; for r

d the mouse to the cur, 'Such a trial, dear

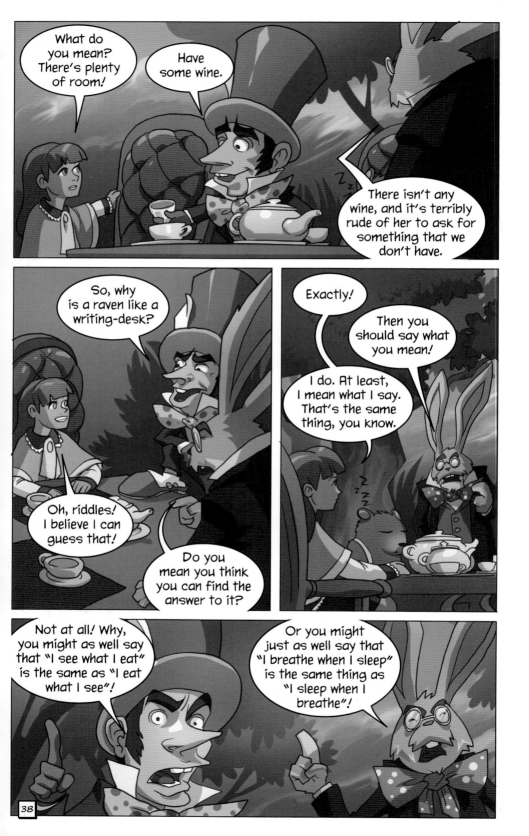

41

CHAPTER 5
The Terrible Queen

42

46

47

CHAPTER 6

The Mock Turtle's Story

53

Carroll's Characters

The Dormouse

"Dormouse" comes from the word *dormeus*, which means "sleepy one." Dormice have very strange sleep patterns. They hibernate for up to six months of every year. They often wake up and eat, then slip back into hibernation. Despite their sleepy tendencies, they are very agile and are well-suited for climbing and jumping.

In *Alice in Wonderland*, the Dormouse is a creature who sleeps through most of the Mad Hatter's tea party. He also makes an appearance during the trial at the end of the book to say that tarts are made of treacle.

The Mad Hatter

Hatters, or hat makers, were considered to be "mad," or crazy, because they used mercury in the production of hats. They regularly touched the mercury, which often led to brain damage from mercury poisoning.

In *Alice in Wonderland*, the Mad Hatter is the host of a tea party that never ends. His guests are the sleepy Dormouse and the March Hare. The "10/6" card that sits in his hat is a price tag that hatters used in their shops. The hat he wears would have sold for ten shillings and six pence in Lewis Carroll's day. That was a lot of money, so it was probably a very nice hat.

Cheshire-Cat

Some cheeses from Cheshire county, Lewis Carroll's home town, were moulded into the shape of a grinning cat. They were known as Cheshire Cat cheeses, and they were cut from the tail end first, leaving the head for last.

In *Alice in Wonderland*, this is similar to the way the Cheshire Cat vanishes, leaving only its smiling face behind. It is believed this is why Lewis Carroll chose to name the strange feline the Cheshire Cat.

Gryphon

The Gryphon in *Alice in Wonderland* is based on the mythical creature that has the body of a lion, and the head and wings of an eagle. They represent strength, intelligence, and fierceness. They are often seen as stone statues that "guard" treasures, like art in a museum.

About the Author

In 1856, Charles Lutwidge Dodgson, also known as Lewis Carroll, met three young children named Edith, Lorina, and Alice Liddell. One day, he took them on a trip in a rowing boat. Carroll thought up a silly story on the spot as they paddled down the river. Young Alice loved the story so much that she asked Carroll to write it down for her. Just like that, the idea for *The Adventures of Alice in Wonderland* was born. Besides writing fiction, Carroll was also an acclaimed mathematician and photographer.

About the Retelling Author

Since 1986, Martin Powell has been a freelance writer. He has written hundreds of stories, many of which have been published by Disney, Marvel, Tekno Comix, Moonstone Books, and others. In 1989, Powell received an Eisner Award nomination for his graphic novel *Scarlet in Gaslight*. This award is one of the highest comic book honours.

About the Illustrator

Daniel Perez was born in Monterrey, Mexico, in 1977. For more than a decade, Perez has worked as a colourist and an illustrator for comic book publishers such as Marvel, Image, and Dark Horse. He currently works for Protobunker Studio and is also developing his own graphic novel.

Glossary

absurdly in a silly or ridiculous way

caucus group or meeting intended to further a cause

croquet outdoor game played by hitting wooden balls with mallets through wire hoops

curious strange or odd

duchess wife or widow of a duke

mad insane

majesty formal title for a king or queen

nonsense silly or meaningless

pity feeling sorry for someone

sorrow great sadness

verdict jury's decision of guilt or innocence

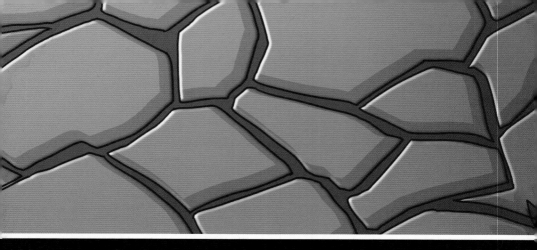

Discussion Questions

1. The world of Wonderland had many strange and interesting creatures. Which character in this book was your favourite? Why?

2. Do you think the King and Queen were good rulers? Why or why not?

3. Which character was most helpful to Alice? In what way did they help her during her journey?

Writing Prompts

1. Alice plays a game called croquet with the Queen. What kinds of games do you like to play? Write about the last time you played a game with some friends or family. Did you have fun? What game was it? Who won?

2. Choose a character from this book, and write about Alice from his or her perspective. Does the character like Alice? Why or why not?

3. Alice's trip to Wonderland was only a dream. What kinds of dreams have you had? Do you ever have nightmares? Write about one of your dreams or nightmares.

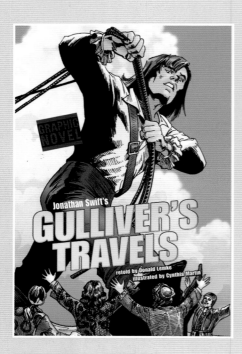

GULLIVER'S TRAVELS

Lemuel Gulliver always dreamed of sailing across seas, but he never could have imagined the places his travels would take him. On the island of Lilliput, he is captured by tiny creatures no more than six inches tall. In the country of Blefuscu, he is nearly squashed by an army of giants. His adventures could be the greatest tales ever told, if he survives long enough to tell them.

THE JUNGLE BOOK

In the jungles of India, a pack of wolves discover a young boy. They name the boy Mowgli and protect him against dangers, including Shere Kan, the most savage tiger in the jungle. As Mowgli grows up, he learns the ways of the jungle from Bagheera the panther, Baloo the wise bear, and other animals. Soon, he must decide whether to remain among beasts or embrace his own kind.

ROBIN HOOD

Robin Hood and his Merrie Men are the heroes of Sherwood Forest. Taking from the rich and giving to the poor, Robin Hood and his loyal followers fight for the downtrodden and oppressed. As they outwit the cruel Sheriff of Nottingham, Robin Hood and his Merrie Men are led on a series of exciting adventures.

THE WIZARD OF OZ

On a bright summer day, a cyclone suddenly sweeps across the Kansas sky. A young girl named Dorothy and her dog, Toto, are carried up into the terrible storm. Far, far away, they crash down in a strange land called Oz. To return home, Dorothy must travel to the Emerald City and meet the all-powerful Wizard of Oz. But the journey won't be easy, and she'll need the help of a few good friends.

Graphic Revolve

If you have enjoyed this story, there are many more exciting tales for you to discover in the Graphic Revolve collection...

20,000 Leagues Under the Sea

Black Beauty

Dracula

Frankenstein

Gulliver's Travels

The Hound of the Baskervilles

The Hunchback of Notre Dame

The Jungle Book

King Arthur and the Knights of the Round Table

Robin Hood

The Strange Case of Dr Jekyll and Mr Hyde

Treasure Island

The War of the Worlds

The Wizard of Oz